JANUARY

DECEMBER
S M T W T F S
                1
2 3 4 5 6 7 8
9 10 11 12 13 14 15
16 17 18 19 20 21 22
23 24 25 26 27 28 29
30 31

FEBRUARY
S M T W T F S
                1 2
3 4 5 6 7 8 9
10 11 12 13 14 15 16
17 18 19 20 21 22 23
24 25 26 27 28

Sunday	Monday	Tuesday	Wednesday	Thursday	Friday	Saturday
		1 New Year's Day	2	3	4	5
6	7	8	9	10	11	12
13	14	15	16	17	18	19
20	21 Martin Luther King, Jr.'s Birthday Observed	22	23	24	25	26
27	28	29	30	31		

FEBRUARY

JANUARY
S M T W T F S
1 2 3 4 5
6 7 8 9 10 11 12
13 14 15 16 17 18 19
20 21 22 23 24 25 26
27 28 29 30 31

MARCH
S M T W T F S
1 2
3 4 5 6 7 8 9
10 11 12 13 14 15 16
17 18 19 20 21 22 23
24 25 26 27 28 29 30
31

Sunday	Monday	Tuesday	Wednesday	Thursday	Friday	Saturday
					1	2
3	4	5	6	7	8	9
10	11	12 Lincoln's Birthday	13 Ash Wednesday	14 Valentine's Day	15	16
17	18	19	20	21	22 Washington's Birthday	23
24	25	26	27	28		

MARCH

FEBRUARY
S M T W T F S
1 2
3 4 5 6 7 8 9
10 11 12 13 14 15 16
17 18 19 20 21 22 23
24 25 26 27 28

APRIL
S M T W T F S
1 2 3 4 5 6
7 8 9 10 11 12 13
14 15 16 17 18 19 20
21 22 23 24 25 26 27
28 29 30

Sunday	Monday	Tuesday	Wednesday	Thursday	Friday	Saturday
					1	2
3	4	5	6	7	8	9
10	11	12	13	14	15	16
17 St. Patrick's Day	18	19	20	21	22	23
24 Palm Sunday	25	26	27	28	29 Good Friday	30 Passover
31 Easter Sunday						

Sky Rocket

APRIL

MARCH

S	M	T	W	T	F	S
					1	2
3	4	5	6	7	8	9
10	11	12	13	14	15	16
17	18	19	20	21	22	23
24	25	26	27	28	29	30
31						

MAY

S	M	T	W	T	F	S
			1	2	3	4
5	6	7	8	9	10	11
12	13	14	15	16	17	18
19	20	21	22	23	24	25
26	27	28	29	30	31	

Sunday	Monday	Tuesday	Wednesday	Thursday	Friday	Saturday
	1	2	3	4	5	6
7	8	9	10	11	12	13
14	15	16	17	18	19	20
21	22	23	24	25	26	27
28	29	30				

MAY

APRIL
S M T W T F S
1 2 3 4 5 6
7 8 9 10 11 12 13
14 15 16 17 18 19 20
21 22 23 24 25 26 27
28 29 30

JUNE
S M T W T F S
1
2 3 4 5 6 7 8
9 10 11 12 13 14 15
16 17 18 19 20 21 22
23 24 25 26 27 28 29
30

Sunday	Monday	Tuesday	Wednesday	Thursday	Friday	Saturday
			1	2	3	4
5	6	7	8	9	10	11
12 Mother's Day	13	14	15	16	17	18
19	20 Victoria Day (Canada)	21	22	23	24	25
26	27 Memorial Day Observed	28	29	30	31	

MAY
S M T W T F S
1 2 3 4
5 6 7 8 9 10 11
12 13 14 15 16 17 18
19 20 21 22 23 24 25
26 27 28 29 30 31

JUNE

JULY
S M T W T F S
1 2 3 4 5 6
7 8 9 10 11 12 13
14 15 16 17 18 19 20
21 22 23 24 25 26 27
28 29 30 31

Sunday	Monday	Tuesday	Wednesday	Thursday	Friday	Saturday
						1
2	3	4	5	6	7	8
9	10	11	12	13	14 Flag Day	15
16 Father's Day	17	18	19	20	21	22
23 30	24	25	26	27	28	29

JULY

JUNE
S M T W T F S
　　　　　　1
2 3 4 5 6 7 8
9 10 11 12 13 14 15
16 17 18 19 20 21 22
23 24 25 26 27 28 29
30

AUGUST
S M T W T F S
　　　　1 2 3
4 5 6 7 8 9 10
11 12 13 14 15 16 17
18 19 20 21 22 23 24
25 26 27 28 29 30 31

Sunday	Monday	Tuesday	Wednesday	Thursday	Friday	Saturday
	1 Canada Day	2	3	4 Independence Day (USA)	5	6
7	8	9	10	11	12	13
14	15	16	17	18	19	20
21	22	23	24	25	26	27
28	29	30	31			

AUGUST

JULY
S M T W T F S
1 2 3 4 5 6
7 8 9 10 11 12 13
14 15 16 17 18 19 20
21 22 23 24 25 26 27
28 29 30 31

SEPTEMBER
S M T W T F S
1 2 3 4 5 6 7
8 9 10 11 12 13 14
15 16 17 18 19 20 21
22 23 24 25 26 27 28
29 30

Sunday	Monday	Tuesday	Wednesday	Thursday	Friday	Saturday
				1	2	3
4	5 Civic Holiday (Canada)	6	7	8	9	10
11	12	13	14	15	16	17
18	19	20	21	22	23	24
25	26	27	28	29	30	31

Rolling Stone

SEPTEMBER

AUGUST
S M T W T F S
            1 2 3
4 5 6 7 8 9 10
11 12 13 14 15 16 17
18 19 20 21 22 23 24
25 26 27 28 29 30 31

OCTOBER
S M T W T F S
         1 2 3 4 5
6 7 8 9 10 11 12
13 14 15 16 17 18 19
20 21 22 23 24 25 26
27 28 29 30 31

Sunday	Monday	Tuesday	Wednesday	Thursday	Friday	Saturday
1	2 Labor Day	3	4	5	6	7
8	9 Rosh Hashana	10	11	12	13	14
15	16	17	18 Yom Kippur	19	20	21
22	23	24	25	26	27	28
29	30					

Grandma's Star

OCTOBER

SEPTEMBER
S M T W T F S
1 2 3 4 5 6 7
8 9 10 11 12 13 14
15 16 17 18 19 20 21
22 23 24 25 26 27 28
29 30

NOVEMBER
S M T W T F S
1 2
3 4 5 6 7 8 9
10 11 12 13 14 15 16
17 18 19 20 21 22 23
24 25 26 27 28 29 30

Sunday	Monday	Tuesday	Wednesday	Thursday	Friday	Saturday
		1	2	3	4	5
6	7	8	9	10	11	12
13	14 Thanksgiving Day (Canada) Columbus Day (USA) Observed	15	16	17	18	19
20	21	22	23	24	25	26
27	28	29	30	31 Halloween		

NOVEMBER

OCTOBER
S M T W T F S
1 2 3 4 5
6 7 8 9 10 11 12
13 14 15 16 17 18 19
20 21 22 23 24 25 26
27 28 29 30 31

DECEMBER
S M T W T F S
1 2 3 4 5 6 7
8 9 10 11 12 13 14
15 16 17 18 19 20 21
22 23 24 25 26 27 28
29 30 31

Sunday	Monday	Tuesday	Wednesday	Thursday	Friday	Saturday
					1	2
3	4	5 Election Day	6	7	8	9
10	11 Remembrance Day (Canada) Veterans Day (USA)	12	13	14	15	16
17	18	19	20	21	22	23
24	25	26	27	28 Thanksgiving Day (USA)	29	30

NOVEMBER
S M T W T F S
1 2
3 4 5 6 7 8 9
10 11 12 13 14 15 16
17 18 19 20 21 22 23
24 25 26 27 28 29 30

DECEMBER

JANUARY
S M T W T F S
1 2 3 4
5 6 7 8 9 10 11
12 13 14 15 16 17 18
19 20 21 22 23 24 25
26 27 28 29 30 31

Sunday	Monday	Tuesday	Wednesday	Thursday	Friday	Saturday
1	2 Hanukkah	3	4	5	6	7
8	9	10	11	12	13	14
15	16	17	18	19	20	21
22	23	24	25 Christmas Day	26 Boxing Day (Canada)	27	28
29	30	31				

Crossing Over Time was designed and made by Joyce Winterton Stewart, a quilter from Rexburg, Idaho.

Crossing Over Time

All pattern pieces include ¼″ seam allowance. All measurements for pieces, sashing, and border strips are given *including* seam allowances, unless otherwise noted. Fabric requirements are based on 44″/45″-wide fabric with trimmed selvages, and requirements for backing are based on a three-panel backing. *Generous allowances are given for fabric requirements to account for fabric shrinkage and individual differences in cutting.* Fabric requirements are given for one-piece borders. We suggest that you wash, dry, and press fabrics before using. Finished quilt size is the size of the quilt before quilting.

Finished Quilt Size
82″ x 102″

Number of Blocks and Finished Size
12 blocks—12″ x 12″

Fabric Requirements for Sampler Blocks

Beige print	— ⅛ yd.
Dk. brown print	— ¼ yd.
Rust print	— ¼ yd.
Lt. teal blue prints	— ⅜ yd. total
Teal blue prints	— ½ yd. total
Dk. teal blue prints	— ½ yd. total
Green floral stripe	— ½ yd.
Green prints	— ⅜ yd. total
Blue prints	— ¼ yd. total
Dk. blue prints	— ½ yd. total
Purple print	— ¼ yd.
Pink*	— 1¼ yd.
Pink prints	— ⅜ yd. total
Dk. pink prints	— ½ yd. total
Mauve prints	— ½ yd. total
Burgundy prints	— ¼ yd. total
Floral prints	— ½ yd. total

*The same pink fabric is used in the connecting blocks and borders. See below for additional fabric requirement.

Fabric Requirements for Sashing, Connecting Blocks, Borders, Binding, and Backing

Lt. teal blue print	— ⅜ yd. + ⅛
Teal blue print	— ⅝ yd. + ⅝
Dk. teal blue print	— ¾ yd. + ½
Dk. blue print	— ¾ yd. + ½
Aqua print	— ⅜ yd.
Blue print	— 1¼ yd.
Blue stripe	— 3 yd.
Burgundy print	— ⅓ yd.
Red print	— ¼ yd.
Mauve print	— ½ yd. + ½
Pink	— 2⅝ yd.
Floral print	— 2½ yd.
Dk. blue for bias binding	— 1¼ yd.
Backing	— 8¾ yd.

Number to Cut for Sampler Blocks

Four Crowns

Template A	— 2 teal blue print
	2 mauve print
Template B	— 4 teal blue print
	4 pink
	4 pink print
Template C	— 8 dk. blue print
	8 burgundy print
	8 pink
Template D	— 4 dk. pink print

Merry Kite

Template A	— 4 dk. teal blue print
	8 pink
Template B	— 4 pink print
Template E	— 4 dk. pink print
	4 blue print
Template E**	— 4 dk. pink print
	4 blue print
Template F	— 1 floral print

**Flip or turn over template if fabric is one-sided.

Joseph's Coat
Template A	— 4 blue print
	4 mauve print
Template C	— 8 pink
Template D	— 4 teal blue print
Template G	— 8 dk. blue print
	8 pink
Template H	— 8 mauve print
Template I	— 4 green floral stripe

Sky Rocket
Template J	— 4 pink
Template J**	— 4 pink
Template K	— 4 dk. pink print
Template L	— 1 burgundy print
	4 green print
Template M	— 4 dk. teal blue print
Template N	— 8 floral print

Aunt Sukey's Choice
Template A	— 4 teal blue print
	8 green print
Template B	— 4 burgundy print
Template E	— 4 beige print
Template E**	— 4 beige print
Template O	— 4 pink
Template O**	— 4 pink

Storm at Sea
Template A	— 4 dk. blue print***
Template C	— 8 pink
	4 dk. blue print
Template D	— 4 green print
Template N	— 4 pink print
Template P	— 4 teal blue print
Template Q	— 4 dk. pink print
Template Q**	— 4 dk. pink print
Template R	— 4 dk. blue print***

***Two different dk. blue prints are used, one for template A and one for template R. See block photograph for the month of June.

St. Louis Star
Template D	— 4 lt. teal blue print
Template S	— 8 pink print
Template T	— 4 purple print
Template U	— 4 teal blue print
	4 mauve print
	8 pink
1" x 6¼" strips	— 4 dk. brown print

Swing in the Center
Template B	— 4 dk. teal blue print
	4 pink
Template C	— 8 pink
	8 dk. teal blue print
Template L	— 1 dk. pink print 3 3/8
	4 blue print
Template V	— 4 dk. pink print
1" x 4½" strips	— 4 floral print

Rolling Stone
Template C	— 8 pink
	4 lt. teal blue print
	4 dk. teal blue print
Template F	— 1 floral print 4½
Template L	— 4 mauve print 3 3/8
Template W	— 4 dk. pink print 2½ x 4½
	4 green floral stripe

Grandma's Star
Template A	— 4 pink print
	4 dk. pink print
	4 mauve print
	4 lt. teal blue print
	4 teal blue print
Template P	— 4 pink
Template Q	— 2 dk. teal blue print
	2 rust print
Template Q**	— 2 dk. teal blue print
	2 rust print

Shoo Fly
Template C	— 12 dk. pink print
	8 floral print
	8 pink
	6 teal blue print
	6 dk. teal blue print
Template D	— 4 dk. teal blue print
	4 green floral stripe

Best of All
Template A	— 8 floral print
	4 dk. teal blue print
Template B	— 8 pink
	4 teal blue print
Template C	— 8 dk. blue print
	8 burgundy print
Template N	— 8 dk. pink print
Template X	— 4 dk. blue print

**Flip or turn over template if fabric is one-sided.

Number to Cut for Sashing, Connecting Blocks, Side and Corner Triangles

Sashing
| 2" x 12½" strips | — 48 pink |
| Template Y | — 31 red print |

Snowflake (Connecting Block)
Template Z	— 24 blue print
Template AA	— 6 aqua print
Template BB	— 24 pink

Side Triangles
Template AA	— 10 aqua print
Template CC	— 20 pink
Template DD	— 20 blue print
Template EE	— 10 blue print

Corner Triangles
Template AA	— 4 aqua print
Template FF	— 8 blue print
Template GG	— 4 pink

Quilt Top Assembly

1. Refer to block photographs and Block Piecing Diagrams for each of the 12 sampler blocks. Join pieces as shown. Make 12 blocks total.

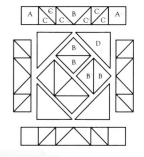

Four Crowns Block Piecing Diagram

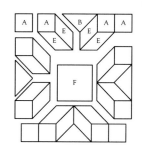

Merry Kite Block Piecing Diagram

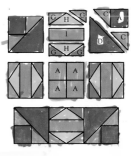

Joseph's Coat Block Piecing Diagram

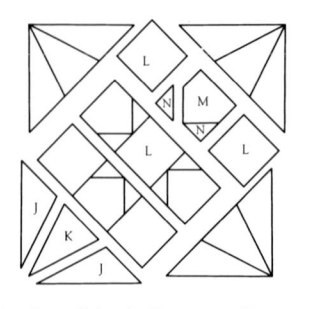

Sky Rocket Block Piecing Diagram

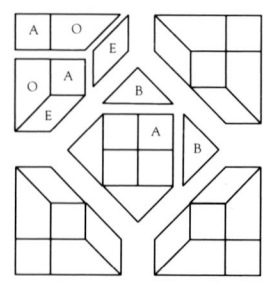

Aunt Sukey's Choice Block Piecing Diagram

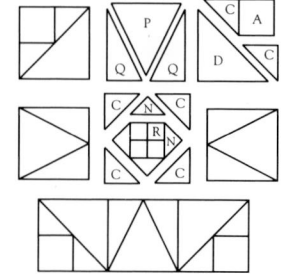

Storm at Sea Block Piecing Diagram

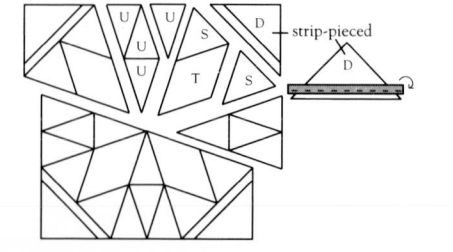

St. Louis Star Block Piecing Diagram

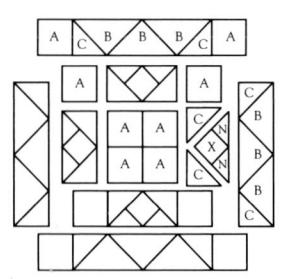

Swing in the Center Block Piecing Diagram

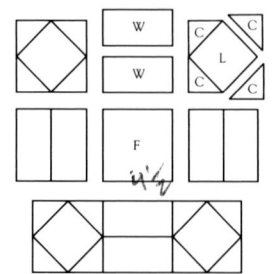

Rolling Stone Block Piecing Diagram

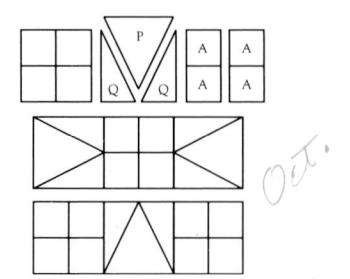

Grandma's Star Block Piecing Diagram

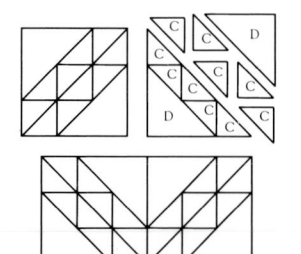

Shoo Fly Block Piecing Diagram

Best of All Block Piecing Diagram

2. The Snowflake block is used as the connecting block. Join pieces Z, AA, and BB, as shown in Snowflake Block Piecing Diagram. Make 6 blocks.

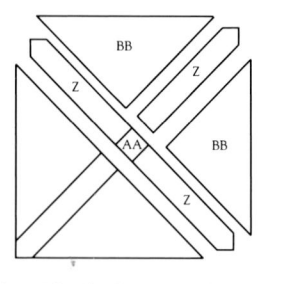

Snowflake Block Piecing Diagram

Setting Diagram I

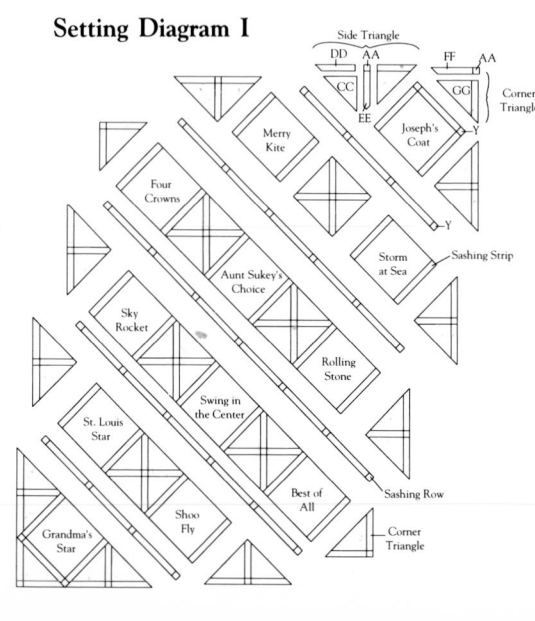

Setting Diagram II

3. Join sashing strips to opposite sides of every sampler block, as shown in Setting Diagram I.

4. Alternate 22 sashing strips with **27** squares (Y) and join to form 5 sashing rows, as shown in Setting Diagram I. [The remaining 4 squares (Y) are used in the corner sections.]

5. Join pieces AA, CC, DD, and EE to form side triangles, as shown in Setting Diagram I. Make 10 side triangles.

Join pieces AA, FF, and GG to form corner triangles. Make 4 corner triangles.

6. Join sashing rows, side triangles, and 1 corner triangle to block rows, as shown in Setting Diagram II.

Make corner sections, as shown. Join rows, sections, and corner triangle, as shown.

7. Cut 4 borders, 2¼″ wide, from floral print. Join to quilt and miter corners.

8. Cut 4 borders, 1⅜″ wide, from blue print. Join to quilt and miter corners.

9. For checkerboard border, cut 2"-wide strips across the grain of each fabric shown in the Chart of Strip-Pieced Panels. For Panel I, cut 2 strips of each fabric to obtain the required number of segments; for Panel II: 3 strips of each fabric; for Panel III: 3 strips of each fabric; for Panel IV: 2 strips of each fabric; for Panel V: 1 strip of each fabric for each time that it is used; and for Panel VI: 1 strip of each fabric for each time that it is used.

Arrange strips in groups of 4 in the order shown in the chart. Join strips lengthwise. Cut *across* seam lines of each panel at 2" intervals for segments. Cut the number of segments from each panel that is indicated on the chart.

10. Arrange segments in border units, as shown in Border Piecing Diagram. (Roman numerals correspond to the panel from which the segment was cut.) Join segments and make 32 units.

Unit

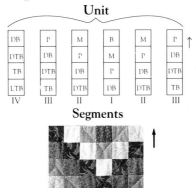

Segments

Border Piecing Diagram
Arrow indicates the top of the unit.

Arrange segments to form corner blocks, as shown in Corner Block Piecing Diagram. Make 4. (You will have 4 segments from Panel IV remaining.)

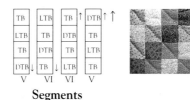

Segments

Corner Block Piecing Diagram
Small arrows indicate the top of each segment, and the large arrow indicates the top of the corner block.

11. Arrange 9 units and 1 segment IV to form border, as shown in Setting Diagram III and quilt photograph. Make sure all units are set in the same direction. Join units and segment, as shown. Make 2 borders and join to opposite sides of quilt.

12. Arrange 7 units and 1 segment IV to form border, as shown in Top and Bottom Border Piecing Diagram and Setting Diagram III. Join units, segment, and corner blocks, as shown. (Note the directional arrows for the corner blocks before joining.) Make 2 borders and join to quilt.

13. Cut 4 borders, 3½" wide, from blue print. Join to quilt and miter corners.

Quilting and Finished Edges
Outline-quilt ¼" from seam lines as a start; then add your favorite quilting designs in large unpieced areas and along the borders. Bind in dk. blue fabric.

Chart of Strip-Pieced Panels

Panel I

Burgundy print	(B) ↑
Mauve print	(M)
Pink	(P)
Dk. blue print	(DB)

Cut 32 - 2" segments.

Panel II

Mauve print	(M) ↑
Pink	(P)
Dk. blue print	(DB)
Dk. teal blue print	(DTB)

Cut 64 - 2" segments.

Panel III

Pink	(P) ↑
Dk. blue print	(DB)
Dk. teal blue print	(DTB)
Teal blue print	(TB)

Cut 64 - 2" segments.

Panel IV

Dk. blue print	(DB) ↑
Dk. teal blue print	(DTB)
Teal blue print	(TB)
Lt. teal blue print	(LTB)

Cut 36 - 2" segments.

Panel V

Dk. teal blue print	(DTB) ↑
Teal blue print	(TB)
Lt. teal blue print	(LTB)
Teal blue print	(TB)

Cut 8 - 2" segments.

Panel VI

Teal blue print	(TB) ↑
Dk. teal blue print	(DTB)
Teal blue print	(TB)
Lt. teal blue print	(LTB)

Cut 8 - 2" segments.

Arrows indicate the top edge of each panel.

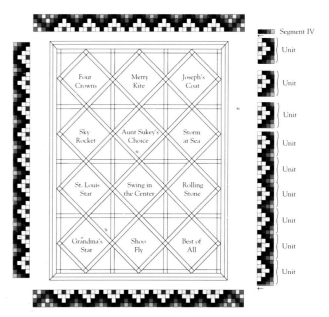

Setting Diagram III

Corner Block | Unit | | | | | | | Segment IV | Corner Block

Top and Bottom Border Piecing Diagram

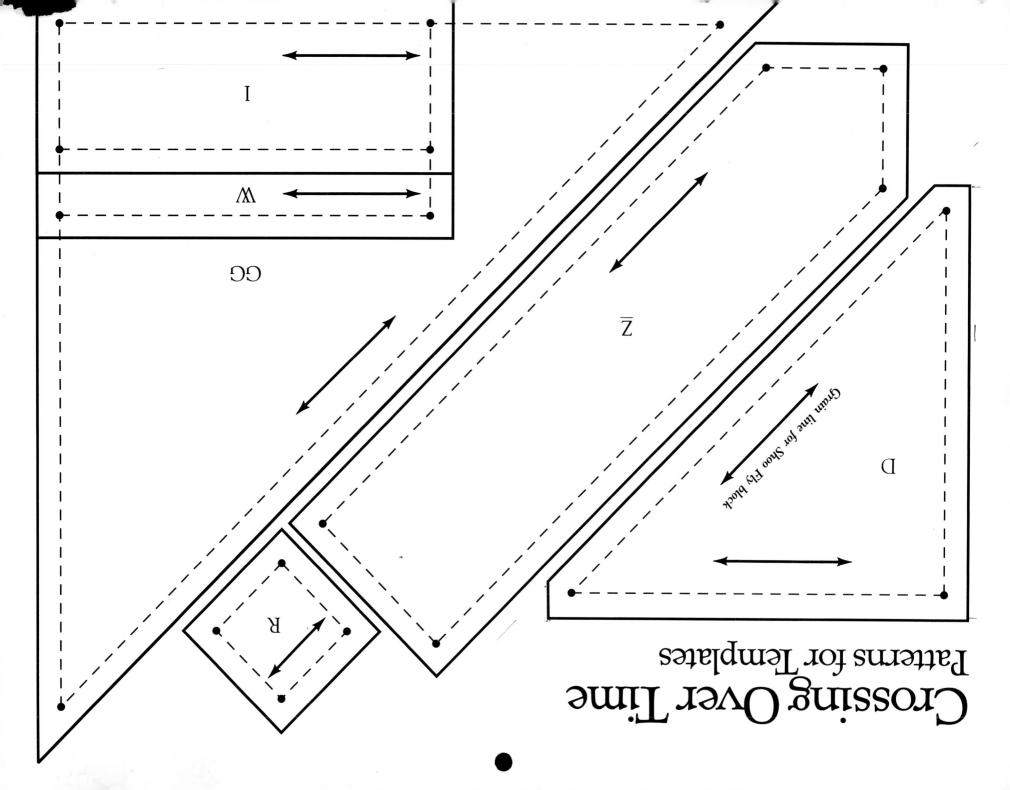

I

W

GG

Z̄

D

Grain line for Shoo Fly block

R

Crossing Over Time
Patterns for Templates

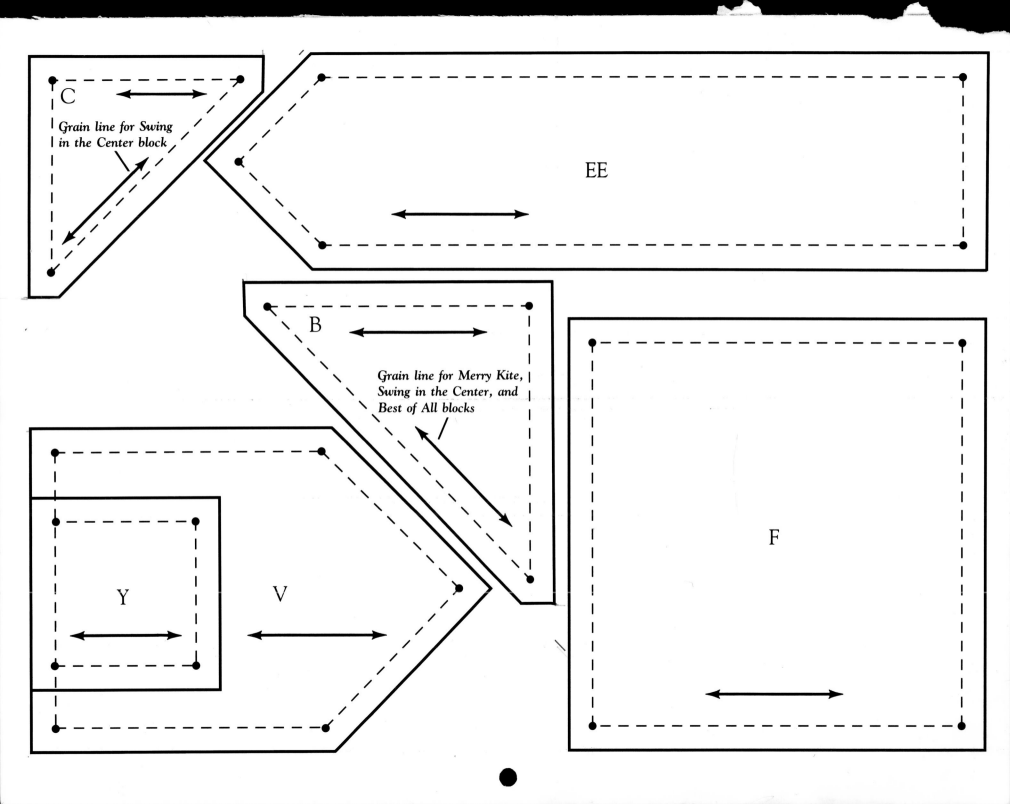

C

Grain line for Swing in the Center block

EE

B

Grain line for Merry Kite, Swing in the Center, and Best of All blocks

Y

V

F

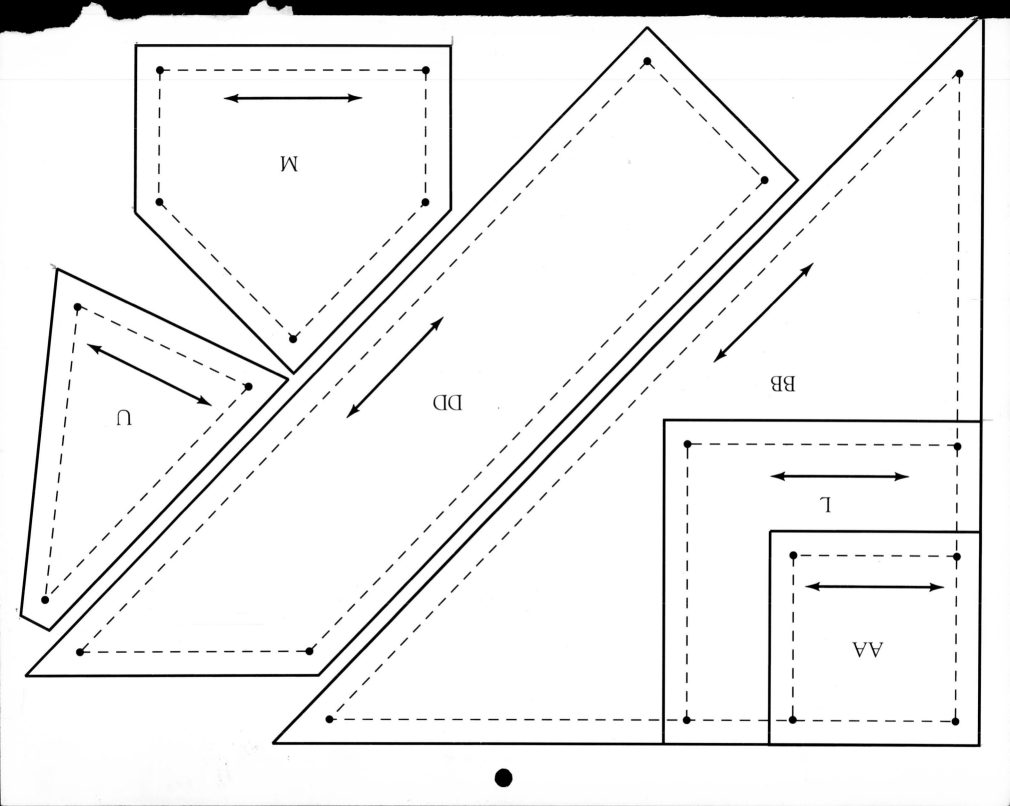

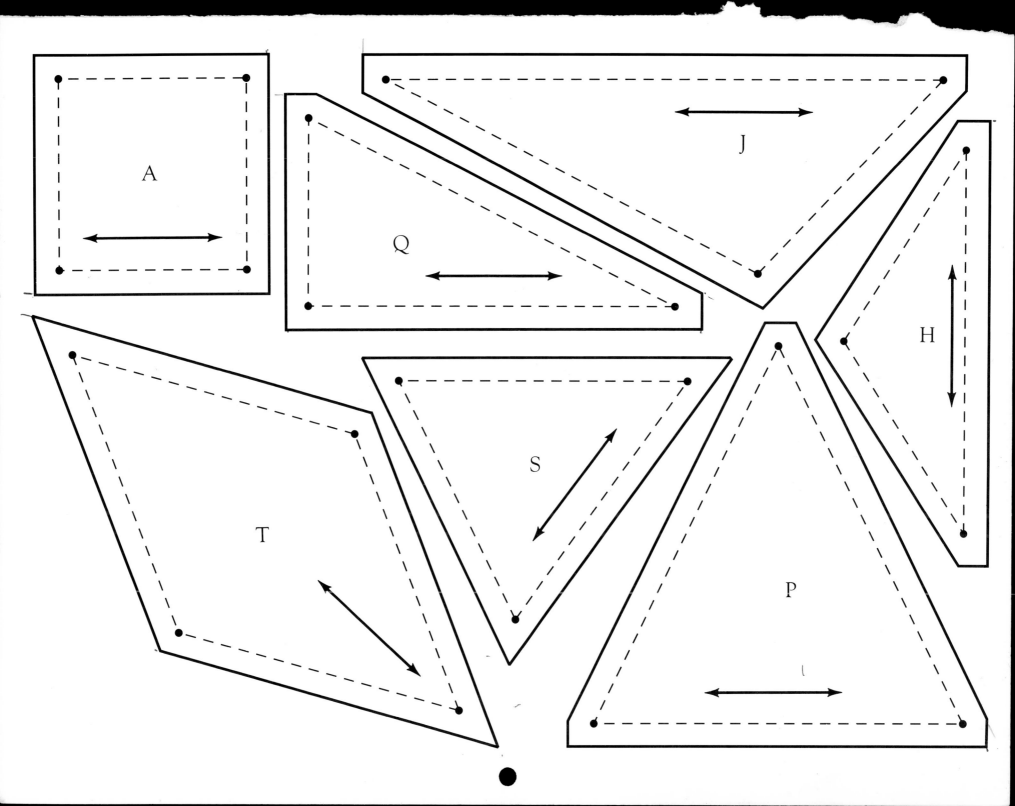

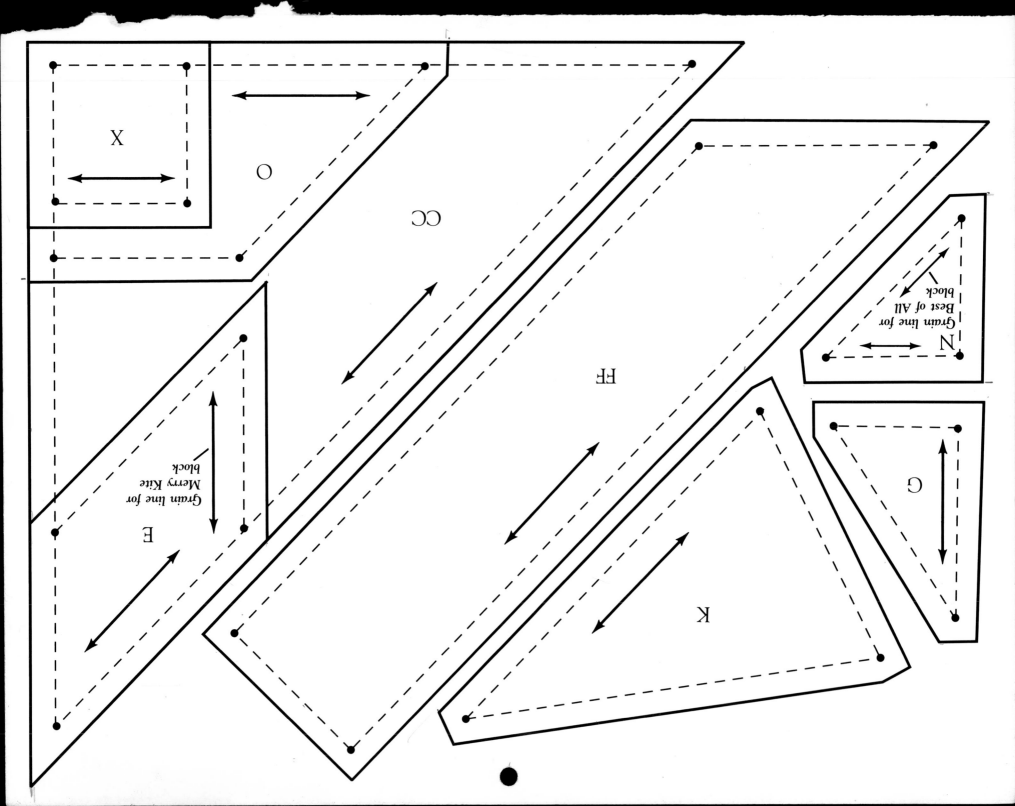